ted handbag,
couldn't find
V. good husband)
= (Leonie Marco
Hermes

The man who wrote the
film or directed....
The Enchanted Cottage
—what a sensitive, ?
and the beautiful idea....
odigliani
Mystical magic
intimate bohemian
affair _____ I'd have had so much to to now

Mr. Cadbury (but for de Roc
Frederico Fellini —
Mountaineer, Mallory, George   earnest moods) —always
Mallory (they found an   for the chocolate.
unpaid bill in his
? Stamp!   jacket pocket on his   'Merlin'' then   Byron
ui alive)   frozen body) Thoroughly   The English Mystics.   Shelley
s played by   decent. Not like that   Mr. Carol Reed   Men and   Keats
ndo).   (not   anymore!!   Baron Von Richtofen   all
Thomas...   Men wouldnt   Mr. Lindberg (aviator)
yet...)   in   want to   Good looking chap to.....
Resistance   Uniform   disappoint him
brave + true
le Dumas   pere   Montgomery Clift   Mr. Gainsborough
le Dumas   fils.   Man Ray
Tati   James Henry Creed, Francis Drake
A Camus Sir Richard Burton,   Perfumer.   Prince Rupert
explorer, linguist, writer   Pete Duel   Ayrton Senna ?
Pete Duel   Marc Bolan...
Raoul Wallenberg   Mr. Martin Luther King   It's Marc of
Shakespeare...   for his whole life... Jim Morrison.
yron   Jimi Hendrix   hero.
Ellery who was that guy nannè Pierre Curie —   Put your hair up. walk in
ats   to Mary Wollstonecraft ?   a room with him,
gorgeous.   sip a cocktail.
wear a white cocktail dress

...chard Burton,
w – top choice for
...ding lost
...ternoons with
any place in
the world
lot of Welsh men
...yed by (There's room in his heart
for all of us......)—why?
should I have missed out
to have experienced the intensity...

Alexander Graham Bell....
I'd never have wanted to
disappoint him... Emile Hermés (
when his w)
a reference "never and all
onesie like
I suppose english Mystics.

Robbie Burns — just because
there were other
wavers
Mr. Keir Hardie — chats!
extraor
and very bright man
ter

The Man who wrote The
film or directed....
The Enchanted Cottage
—what a sensitive, ? ?
beautiful idea...
Mystical magic....
writer, journalist have had so much to say
played to him.

very nice Michael
Landon of Little House in
the Prairie, writer + star
– best of old America, he'd
have helped build
the school house etc.
Good husband material

Zapata
marlon B
Miche
dea
Frend
Alexai
Alexan
Jacqu

Mr. Edward Munch for
sensitivity — would he
be too sensitive as a
boyfriend?

...ice Rainytsinji – played to him. lived
...icket for England. lived
in hotel in Brighton
...ayboy prince Gitmour Albert Camus, writer, journalist,
footballer....

...olph Nureyev — as Pierre Curie —
...ernoon fawn" — how Husbands who supported
...e felt like the the suffragettes. Cary Grant
...en of the fairies an All the men who
good days... were supportive in the
....es of the suffragettes.

Dumas.
La dame
and
camelias
Rubens
Modigliani
Munch

TIME TRAVEL BOYFRIENDS w56

by Josephine Halbert

Published by Zed Said 2007
29 Kings Road
Whitley Bay
Tyne and Wear
NE26 3BD

Text and Illustrations – © *Josephine Halbert 2007*
Commissioning Editor – *Helen Limon, Zed Said Books*
Art Design Consultant – *Gary Prosser*
Book and Cover Design – *Park Studio*
'Pin ups/If you were mine…' Text – © *Alicia Foster 2007*

Printed by Finger prints, Barrow-in-Furness, Cumbria

ISBN   9780955104930

TIME TRAVEL BOYFRIENDS

by Josephine Halbert

with a foreword by Alicia Foster

PIN UPS/IF YOU WERE MINE...

In *The Pursuit of Love* Nancy Mitford evokes the vivid fantasy and hopeless longing that make up the inner worlds of teenage girls. 'We were, of course, both in love, but with people we had never met; Linda with the Prince of Wales, and I with a fat, red-faced, middle-aged farmer, who I sometimes saw riding through Shenley. These loves were strong, and painfully delicious; they occupied all our thoughts...' Josephine Halbert, talking of her aunts – who were girls at around the same time as Mitford – recalls their enduring love of the film star, Ronald Colman. Their sense of intimacy with their favourite was such, Halbert says, that when they talked about their idol, it felt as if he had just been for tea.

As an artist who makes films, Halbert has found some crucial influences in the cinema – the surreal, supernatural strangeness and intense colour of the work of Powell and Pressburger is echoed in Halbert's *Shadow Buddy*, (2002); the weird, outsize chair, the hot pink silk that floats in and out of focus, the sea – a powerful metaphor for emotional life (used so memorably in Powell and Pressburger's *A Matter of Life and Death* and *I Know Where I'm Going*). And then there is the invisible friend made flesh in *Shadow Buddy*, the perfect boy who existed in Halbert's childhood imagination, and who she materialised in her art years later.

The men who make up the gallery of desire that is *Time Travel Boyfriends* are, in a sense, the elder brothers of *Shadow Buddy* – the grown-ups Halbert graduated on to. They are a fascinating group – at first glance rather diverse, they have in common a certain buccaneering bravado, a love of showmanship and of striking a pose – from Elmer Clifton's hysteric-dandy swagger, to Grey Owl's replendent, romantic fakery.

Returning to the obsessions, make-believe and games of her past, Halbert is part of a strong current in recent art – Niki de Saint Phalle, Tracey Emin and Lucy Gunning are among those who have mined their intimate girlhood histories. And Freud has taught us all the importance of childhood, that the emotions and imaginings experienced then shape the adult. With *Time Travel Boyfriends* Halbert summons up youthful daydreams, playing the female lead opposite her pin-ups-lover, muse, rescuer. But there is also a sense of a girl living out fantasies of gripping adventure and spot-lit glamour vicariously through men's lives. There is a dark side to fantasy; it acts as a panacea for the losses life inflicts upon us

– when existence is difficult, restricted, painful, the fantasy figure becomes essential (think of Anne Frank's hiding place in Amsterdam – the only respite from the dreary room, her precious collection of postcards and magazine cuttings – films stars, royalty – pasted upon the wall). The juxtaposition of Halbert's hazy, sketched girl and the immaculate, crisply focussed men represents the seductive but dangerous power of the image – he is more real to her than her own self.

She contemplates his picture; she dreams. One day – imagine it – he might catch sight of her in the street, notice her at a party; he might come for tea, somehow… and stay.

Alicia Foster

Alicia Foster is an art historian, writer and lecturer whose published works include *Gwen John* (1999), and *Tate Women Artists* (2004). She is currently working on a new critical study of Gwen John for Yale University Press, a biography of Laura Knight, and a book about women during the Second World War.

TIME TRAVEL BOYFRIENDS

Elmer Clifton started it. He jumped out of a book I was reading in the British Film Institute Library and I just knew him at once. There was something familiar about this zany character from the world of silent films striking a theatrical pose with his firestarter look and I realised if I'd been around when he had he was JUST the type of guy I would go and get involved with.

This triggered thoughts about other 'men' from the past. So I followed my bliss and started my own Time Travel Dating Agency. Lightheartedly playing with the idea, I wrote lists of inspiring but very dead men. There were a lot to choose from. Some, maddeningly, turned out to be still alive and so were exempt from consideration – or at least in this edition! This collection is not necessarily a line-up of my ideal romantic loves but a group of men whose appeal is as diverse as the sides of myself (as are anyone else's) and are the focus of a mood, a memory or a particular longing. We can time-travel back in our own lives to significant moments and evoke their atmospheres or the past will find us somewhere lingering in one of its familiar rooms. These hauntings can be pleasant or not. There are many avenues and choices and many characters to meet along the way.

As time went on I realised that this was about myself and not about the men at all. We can all muse forever about lives we may have had in other times but it always comes down to the fact that whenever and with whoever, we would always be… OURSELVES! This could be my own personal 'coping mechanism' about love, loss, disappointment, hope, experience… all of this we humans know when we are trying to make the sense we cannot make of it. The day dream resulted in this book… an indulgence…

The men in this book are mainly from the early to mid-20th Century. There is a familiarity to our grandparents' era but also a safe distance – we can do our own 'mythical' edit of lives truly lived among the sepia photos – not so far from our contemporary world. Also, we grow up in the shadow of their dreams, inspired by their wish-list of heroes and heroines and enjoy its nostalgia. I needed some personal and cultural connection which rang true when considering these men even if I did dream further from home… Crazy Horse, for instance, with his reputedly handsome and perfect symmetrical face and bravery has his obvious attractions… but would I really want to live in a teepee in the American mid-west in those winters? No. But, Grey Owl, the self-invented Apache persona of Archibald Belaney from Kent who went to live in Canada in the early 20th Century appeals to the English eccentric in me... I can imagine sharing his cabin with a few well loved classics to read by the log fire and staring up at the stars together beyond the giant trees from his canoe.

It's hard to avoid the power of the early Hollywood influence before the 'now' celebrity culture and its lack of mystery... I'd like to have sat next to Orson Welles in his heyday in a sports car in the Riviera when I'd be old enough to handle the worldly stuff but impressionable enough to be star-struck... and get caught up in its tornado.

I don't want to dwell on the dark side of these playmates or their realities. This is fantasy, after all...

I want to see Robert Browning, the rescuer, who becomes your only family as you journey off to Italy on a wing and prayer but together. I want to ride in the ancient chariots of Robert Graves' mind in his Mediterranean paradise, enveloped by the scent of jasmine where our dreams would be real to us and I'd be his muse of the moment. I'd like to call my soulmate Jim Morrison in the middle of the night and suggest a poet's tour somewhere or just round at my place, the agony and ecstasy of waiting for him to arrive as the 'other' world sleeps, our next few hours charmed by lamplight and the generosity of the fairies. My earth would move as Charles Fry turned round and looked me straight in the eyes as he marched down the steps to take his turn at the wicket, adjusting his gloves, the sun shining and the spectators applauding. I can imagine the energy of a young Brunel sharing his 'visions' with me, and stealing away on the night train to Inverness with the eternally romantic Robert Donat, young and beautiful forever on golden hued celluloid, us sharing a cigarette and a hip flask by the window in the train in our beautiful clothes. I want to laugh out loud with the earthy James Martin and breathe deep with him among the elements.

And Marlon Brando – I'd like to have met him straight off the set of *A Streetcar Named Desire* wearing that torn t-shirt.

I dedicate this book to the Unknown Man.

Josephine Halbert

ELMER CLIFTON

(1890 – 1949)
Actor / Director

Elmer Clifton found himself working in silent films in Hollywood's early years after being discovered while on a tour with a theatrical troupe by D.W. Griffith (THE film director of the era). Clifton could be described as the first 'method actor' – he was said to display a range of emotions and a masculine heroism unknown before in films, though this went apparently entirely unnoticed by the critics of the time. He became a gifted and capable director, his only independent production, his dream epic on whaling, *Down to the Sea in Ships* (1923) was a whole year in the making and made a star of Clara Bow… (It was perhaps inspired by his remote upbringing on an island on St. Lawrence River). Clifton seemed to be either ahead of his time or in the wrong time – after *Down to the Sea in Ships*, the Wall Street Crash abruptly ended his chances of more lavish independent productions. In spite of this, the popular and resourceful Clifton carried on making movies for Hollywood studios and was to take his last breath in 'the director's chair'. His films are still available today as are his performances in D.W. Griffith's films *Intolerance* (1916) and *Birth of a Nation* (1915). He was married and had children.

Dear Gwen Clifton
I just wanted to
let you know that
if I'd been around
too in 1916 — I'd
have really gone
for you

CHARLES BURGESS FRY

(1872 – 1956)
Sportsman / Writer / Journalist / Politician / Model

An Edwardian, all-round hero, Fry's sporting achievements
(he represented England in three sports including cricket)
were matched by academic promise and beauty (it was said
he looked like he'd walked straight out of a frieze from the
Elgin Marbles). A legendary man's man, Fry cut a dash in
many influential and glamorous circles, and such was the
hero-worship at the time, was rumoured to have been offered
the kingdom of Albania... which he declined. He had his own
magazine and was a 'celebrity' face for advertising in the
pre-professional days of first class sport. Later he stood
for Parliament, joined the League of Nations and even pursued
a Hollywood career in his fifties.

This 'complex' and handsomest of men's choice of bride raised
eyebrows in those more rigid times. Beatrice Holme Sumner
(said to be of royal descent) was ten years his senior and the
longterm lover of a rich, married man with whom she'd had
children. Many thought she was 'awful' and 'dominant' but
Fry called her 'his Madame' and the two ran a charity started
by her former lover to make amends for his ways (a pre-sea
training ship for 'poor boys of good character' where the
'sporty' Beatrice appeared to be in her element). They had
children and wrote a novel together. Fry's autobiography
is entitled 'Life Worth Living'.

JIM MORRISON

(1943 – 1971)

Poet / Philosopher / Singer

Jim Morrison became a legend in his own short lifetime as a poet-libertine-hero whose life in the fast lane challenged any boundaries in his way. Famed as the voice of the passionate and original music of *The Doors*, he has an eternal, iconic appeal.

Morrison had a strict upbringing in an itinerant US military family (his father became naval attaché to London). Described as a charming, sensitive and magnetic boy by his teachers and schoolfriends, he grew into a charismatic beauty with a thirst for knowledge. As a student he was influenced by an eclectic mix of ideas from the worlds of philosophy, religion, mysticism and literature. He found his epic voice in Venice Beach, California when he met the fellow creatives with whom he created *The Doors* as lyricist and vocalist for their unique style of music. The band quickly won a place in the world's rock elite, fronted by Morrison's charismatic, dramatic performances.

After five years of fame and all its ramifications, Morrison had hit the self-destruct button and took time out to write (he published his poetry), going to Paris with Pamela Courson, his longterm soul-mate and 'number one' girlfriend. He tragically died there and is buried in the Père Lachaise cemetery only weeks after his visit to its gravesides of Chopin, Balzac and Oscar Wilde.

Dear Jim,
I'm not sure it would
have lasted but I am
sure it would have been
one of those soul-mate
things .... and it would
have been ours.... forever ♡

BRUNEL

(1806 – 1859)
Engineer / Designer

Isambard Kingdom Brunel followed his successful, French
father into the world of design and engineering, carving out
his own remarkable career in the midst of the British industrial
revolution. This pint-sized, energetic genius found himself
in the right place at the right time, a shining example of the
Victorian can-do culture and is remembered as one of the
most eminent men of his era. His work is with us today
(*The Great Western Railway* and the *The Clifton Suspension
Bridge*, just two of his creations).

Brunel benefited from a secure, affectionate, bilingual
upbringing with an international outlook – far from the norm
in British 'society' at the time. This appeared to cause him
some difficulty adjusting to the wider world of his peers in his
youth when he had a certain period of unhappiness in love and
a loss of direction but later on he accepted the conventions of
the day, marrying a 'statuesque beauty from an artistic family'
and set about building his career. He found time to enjoy
fatherhood and family life while in the throws of working on
his heroic industrial undertakings – all devised on four hours
sleep a night and under a constant cloud of cigar smoke (it's
said he smoked up to 40 a day).

Dear Brunel
Actually, I think you could've been
≡ THE ONE ≡.
. It's the way you did things.
I need space in my relationships and you'd have been away a lot. Perfect!

ROBERT GRAVES

(1895 – 1985)

Poet / Novelist / Scholar / Translator

Robert Graves was so badly wounded at the Somme in World War One, he was officially reported dead. He recovered but was shellshocked and was never hospitalised for it like his friend Siegfried Sassoon. His 'realistic' war poems *Over The Brazier* were published in 1916.

He married Nancy Nicholson (sister of artist, Ben) and took up academic posts including one at Cairo University where he was joined by his wife, children and the American poet Laura Riding with whom Graves had fallen in love and moved in, flaunting convention. Riding, instrumental in his recovery from shellshock, became his muse, exerting a great influence. An intense emotional time back in London resulted in Graves leaving to live with Riding (who'd attempted suicide) to Majorca where they wrote academic works together and he wrote his autobiography *Goodbye to All That* (1929) (which brought him money but lost him friends). More success came with a biography of T.E. Lawrence and historical novels, including *I Claudius*. Graves and Riding went to America at the outbreak of the Spanish Civil War. They continued their 'volatile' relationship but later split up.

Returning to Britain, he met Beryl Hodge, then the wife of writer Alan Hodge. They later married and went back to Majorca in 1946, setting up home in Deya and had children, remaining there for the rest of his life, making occasional trips abroad which included a poetry professorship in Oxford in the 1960s. He and Beryl are buried in Deya. Among his 140 published lifetime works is his 'historical grammar of poetic myth' *The White Goddess* (1948) inspired by his experience of Laura Riding and which has never been out of print.

Dear Robert Graves
We could've talked
about Rome and
Caesar himself in
your Mediterranean
paradise... Just you
and I... And we'd
both know that
Caesar was only a
man ... as you were..
Josephine

GREY OWL / WA-SHA-QUON-ASIN

(1888 – 1938)
Writer / Conservationist

Archibald Stansfield Belaney was born and brought up in
Hastings. As a child he showed an interest in nature and Native
American culture. After emigrating to Canada as a young man,
he reinvented himself as the son of a Scottish fur-trapper
father and an Apache mother (it's said he spent hours in front
of mirrors practising 'genuine' Apache expressions). He worked
as a ranger, guide and fur-trapper. This identity endured for
the rest of his life. During World War One he fought in Europe
as a sniper with the Montreal Black Watch and was treated
as an Indian by his compatriots, receiving praise for his part
and as a wounded hero. Later, back in Canada, his third wife,
Gertrude Bernard, an Iroquois woman he later called
Anahareo, encouraged him to write his books on wilderness
life. He wrote them in their cabin Beaver Lodge, by the
Ajawan Lake.

He became a 'personality' in the 1930s and toured widely,
promoting his pioneering environmentalist work and Native
American culture and even visited Buckingham Palace.
Doubts about his identity surfaced after his death… creating
embarrassment, shock and a decline in popularity but recently,
there's been a renewed interest in this intriguing man's life
from filmmakers and conservationists alike… and some of
his works have been republished.

ORSON WELLES

(1915 – 1985)

Actor / Writer / Artist / Director / Narrator / Magician

Orson Welles' unconventional upbringing sparked a rollercoaster of a life and career that had many manifestations in the arts and entertainment industry for decades. His meteoric rise was built on bravado, brilliance and his need to try the impossible, all fuelled by titanic energy (he had even hired ambulances in New York to get around). The young man who shunned college in favour of a painting trip to Ireland, made and starred in his first feature film *Citizen Kane* (1941) with complete artistic control when he was only twenty five; a commercial failure in its day but is now thought by some to be the best film ever made. Welles lived and worked in Europe where he received critical acclaim for his box-office disappointments in the USA (though he was later to return and receive its prestigious Lifetime Achievement Award). His innovation in film including his powerful Shakespearean productions is an important influence on modern cinema. Welles' portrayal of Harry Lime (he insisted on playing the role without make-up) in Carol Reed's brilliant *The Third Man* (1949) is one of his most iconic screen roles and an enduring favourite of many.

Always the outsider and innovator, this bon viveur's personal world mirrored his larger than life career. He had three marriages and his endless talents included an uncanny gift for fortune-telling and a Magic Circle membership which he always kept as something to fall back on and used it to entertain the troops in World War Two.

Dear Orson
You said it was a
fault in your nature
always having to be
bigger than life.....
I'd call that ego these
days, darling but
at least I would
never be bored.....

ROBERT BROWNING

(1812 – 1889)
Poet / Playwright

The London born Browning had an artistic and literary upbringing and is as famous for his dramatic verse as for eloping with the poet Elizabeth Barrett who he met after writing her a fan letter. Six years older than Browning and already well-known for her work, Barrett found in him a twin spirit and a ticket to freedom away from the gloomy prospects of life as an invalid in a suffocating Victorian household ruled by her father, a 'tyrant' who wanted none of his children to marry. Her talent brought her a new life, Browning married his 'idol' and they went to Italy taking her dog 'Flush' with them. They spent years there, became part of its literary and ex-pat circles and had a child.

Browning outlived Elizabeth and went on to find success and fortune with his writing (which was thought to be 'experimental' at the time). Their much celebrated love-story still warms hearts today and has inspired many a sentimental tribute and even some commercial memorabilia – an edition of the lovers' clasped hands in bronze was among the must-have collectors' items of the era.

Lewis

Dear Robert Browning, I a fan.
You wrote your love letter and the rest is history.
Let's make history repeat itself..... but only if
my little dog can come too...

ROBERT DONAT

(1905 – 1958)
Actor / Director

British filmstar and director of the 1930s and 1940s who
was described as the 'most graceful' actor of his time,
Robert Donat was blessed with romantic, leading man's looks
and a distinctive mellifluous voice (the result of elocution
lessons to overcome a childhood stammer). Brought up in
Manchester, the son of a Polish father and English mother,
he was encouraged to go on the stage to overcome a lack of
confidence and poor health which plagued him his whole life.
Success in the theatre led to a career in the burgeoning British
cinema of the 1930s when he enjoyed a period of golden fame
after roles in films such as *The Citadel*, Hitchcock's *The 39
Steps* and *Goodbye Mr. Chips*.

He was a reluctant star and disliked Hollywood, preferring
life in England. His empathetic screen presence, charm and
gentle masculinity has won him many admirers. He is a manly
hero who shows his vulnerability. An inner struggle with his
confidence and the illness that ended his career and short
life only serves to increase his allure as the eternal, sensitive
gentleman hero of any age. He married twice and was re-united
with his first wife before his death.

Dear Robert
you said aching was just
a "puff of smoke" to
you. One person's
puff of smoke is
another's whole
world . . . . .

JAMES MARTIN

(1889 – 1940)

Seaman / Soldier / Explorer / War Hero

James Martin pursued a life of adventure. The one-time Grenadier Guards officer served with the last of the British square riggers in the Australian grain trade, learned dog-driving in Canada and was boatswain on the Antarctic exploration voyages led by Sir Douglas Mawson from 1929-1931. Described as a 'Jekyll and Hyde' character, one moment a 'dapper' guards officer and the next 'a Cape Horn shellback in his denims, cap and pipe', Martin comes across as a 'true' character and 'his own man' in any environment. Nicknamed Lofty because of his height, he was liked for his sense of humour and charming company.

He attracted attention on a polar Discovery voyage for his part in the dramatic rescue of the ship's mascot Blackie the cat, who fell overboard into icy waters during a pronounced roll of the ship. Martin jumped in after her but it was to no avail. Luckily, another seaman, supended on a bowline, grabbed her as she swam back towards the ship. Martin supervised her lengthy recovery in the engine room and when back on dry land, presented one of her kittens to Lady Mawson, his expedition leader's wife.

James Martin was lost at sea in 1940 when his ship was torpedoed and, according to his commanding officer, was 'last seen going down below into the 'tween decks to check everyone was on deck.'.

Dear Seaman Martin
You went off exploring the
seas and you put other
lives before your own
and you still had
time for a cat. I'd have
always had time for you....

MARLON BRANDO

(1924 – 2004)

Actor / Director / Human Rights Activist

No-one had ever seen anyone like the young Marlon Brando
in his early, rawly sensitive, instinctive, 'truthful' performances.
His roles in films such as *On The Waterfront* and *A Streetcar
Named Desire* left audiences, especially women, mesmerised.
He exuded a powerful sexuality, unpredictability and
extraordinary beauty. His role in *The Wild One* (1954) inspired
a blossoming American youth culture amidst the boom of the
1950s, sending sales of leather jackets and jeans into orbit.

Always an individualist, Brando used his fame to promote
his heartfelt human rights causes. He married three 'exotic'
beauties and was the lover of many. His personal tragedies
are well-known. He braved roles that brought him ridicule,
applause or only money and he showed skill as a director.
His inimitable talent had the power to command insanely
huge fees and devotion from admirers right up to the end
in spite of his going off limits of the Hollywood beauty ideal.
Many found him self-destructive and impossible to work with
but others praised his supportiveness and easy company.
But for all his contradictions, the boy brought up in Omaha,
Nebraska, changed the course of modern acting and was
a one-off.

Dear Marlon
when you switched
that magic on, the
camera truly
loved you. If
you'd switched it
on for me I'd
have given you
more than any
camera ever could...

UNKNOWN MAN

JOSEPHINE HALBERT

Josephine Halbert is an artist who has most recently worked with print and filmmaking; writing, producing and directing her own independent productions. Her short films include *Shadow Buddy* (2002), her first dramatic narrative, which was a tribute to her childhood imaginary friend, and *When It Suits Me* (2000), an animated film based on her book of the same name, which have been screened at galleries and film festivals internationally. She exhibits with Beverley Knowles Fine Art, London and Lowood Gallery, Cumbria.

Time Travel Boyfriends is her second book. She lives in London and Northumberland and dreams of having a King Charles Spaniel of her own.

Sincerely yours, Josephine

Author photograph by Alexander Wong

THANK YOU TO

Betty Taylor of the Grey Owl Society, Ursula Frei and Wolfgang Frei of the Edward Quinn Archive, and Nicholas Sharp for their kind permission to use their images.

Thanks also to Neil Robinson of the Marylebone Cricket Club Library, Rob Boddie and Hugh Griffith of Sussex County Cricket Club Library, Monique Ritchie of Brunel University Library, the Nancy Mitford Estate, Charlotte Grant of Christies Images, Stacey Smithson of Getty Images, Mark Dowd at Topfoto and John Cahoon of the Natural History Museum of Los Angeles County.

Special thanks to Gavin Watson, Amy Odell, Alwyn Daniel, Andrew Bottomley, Richard Taylor, Bakul Patki, Margaret O'Brien, Claire Forsyth, Jolyon Thomas, Michael Pulley, Alicia Foster, Jeremy Latimer, Rona Levin... and to my family and friends and anyone who listened!!

Very special thankyous to Helen Limon of Zed Said who suggested this idea could be a book, to Beverley Knowles of Beverley Knowles Fine Art who suggested it could be a show and to Gary Prosser for all his help and support.